THE MYSTERY
OF THE ISLAND

JULES VERNE

Simplified and brought within the vocabulary of
New Method Supplementary Readers, Stage 2, by

MICHAEL WEST
M.A., D.PHIL.

Illustrated by Christopher Evans

LONGMAN

LONGMAN GROUP LIMITED
London

*Associated companies, branches and representatives
throughout the world*

First published in this series 1938
New edition 1967
New impressions 1969; *1970;
*1973; *1974 (twice);
*1976 (with corrections);
*1977

ISBN 0 582 53429 1

The Publishers are indebted to La Librairie Hachette for
their kind permission to reproduce this simplified
translation.

Note: Words with a star* are outside stage 2 of the New
Method Supplementary Readers and are not explained
in the text. These extra words are in a use on page 40.

*Printed in Hong Kong by
Dai Nippon Printing Co (H.K.) Ltd*

CONTENTS

A mystery is a surprising thing, a thing of which you do not know the cause.

The balloon went up again into the sky

One

DROPPED FROM THE SKY

There were four men and a boy and a dog in a balloon.* The balloon was over the sea.

"Is the balloon going up?" said Harding.

"No," said Spillet, "it is going down. It is falling."

"Throw out some water,"[1] said Harding.

"There is not any more water," answered Spillet.

"Then throw everything out," said Harding.

They threw out everything—the guns, the food, the money—everything.

The balloon began to go up.

It was six in the morning. Two hours passed. It was now eight.

"Are we going up?" asked Harding again.

"No, we are falling," said Spillet, "We shall fall into the sea!"

"We must cut off the basket of the balloon!" said Harding. "Climb up into the net and let the basket fall!"

The four men and the boy and the dog climbed up into the net. The basket fell into the sea!

The balloon went up again into the sky.

---

[1]Water is used to give weight to a balloon at the beginning of a journey. In time the gas goes out of the balloon. Then the balloon begins to fall. Water is thrown out; this makes the balloon go up again.

Three hours passed. It was twelve. Again the balloon began to fall.

"What can we throw out now?" cried Spillet. "We must do something to make the balloon go up. We are near the sea. We shall fall into the water."

Harding jumped from the net into the sea. His dog jumped into the sea after him. The balloon had lost the one man and the dog; so it went up again.

The island was now near, but the balloon was falling. It fell. It touched the ground; it went up again. Again it touched. The three men and the boy jumped down onto the ground. The balloon went up. It was lost in the sky.

Who were these men who have come to the island? There were four men and a dog.

(1) There was Gideon Spillet. He was a writer*— he wrote for the *New York Times*. He was a big man with red hair.

(2) There was Pencroft, a seaman*.

(3) The boy was Pencroft's son.

(4) Neb was a black man. He was Harding's servant.

(5) Harding was a learned man. He was a very brave man. (It was Harding who jumped into the sea.)

(6) Top was Harding's dog. The dog jumped into the sea with Harding.

Two

FOOD, WATER AND A HOME

Spillet, Pencroft, Herbert and Neb were on the island. It was a small island, near it was a larger island. On this small island there were no trees; there was no water. There was nothing; but on the larger island there were trees and hills, and little rivers came down the hills into the sea.

Between the two islands there was sea. The men must go across this piece of sea so as to reach the larger island. Neb was looking for Harding. He threw himself into the water. The others looked at him. They could not see him.—No! There he is! He is near the other side. There he is! He is on the other island. He has got across.

Spillet, Pencroft and Herbert crossed the water and came to the big island.

Neb had gone to look for Harding.

Spillet went up the hill to look at the island, and see if there were men and houses.

Pencroft and Herbert walked by the sea. They wanted to find food. They came to some rocks.

"Ha!" cried Pencroft, "I have found some food."

"Where is the food?" said Herbert. "I cannot eat rocks."

"You cannot eat rocks," said Pencroft, "but you can eat the shell fish* which grow on the rocks.—

Now we must find a house. See those rocks. They make the sides of a house. We must build a wall of stones at the north end. We will make a wall of branches* at this end. That will make a nice house."

Pencroft and Herbert built a wall on the north side of the house. Then they went to the forest to get branches. They pulled down branches from the trees in the forest. They got many large branches but they did not know how to carry the branches to the house.

"What shall we do?" said Herbert, "we cannot carry the branches, and we have no donkey, no cart, no motor-car!"

"We have a river," said Pencroft. "Throw the branches in the water. The water will carry them for us."

The branches went down the river*. They went near to the place where the house was. Pencroft and Herbert made a door for the house.

The house was ready!

Three

SPILLET AND NEB COME BACK

"What have we got to eat?" asked Herbert.

"There are shell fish," said Pencroft.

"I have got some eggs!" said Herbert. "I found them in the forest. But what shall we cook them in?"

"In a coconut*!" said Pencroft. "We can cook

They made a fire and cooked the eggs

them in a coconut. But we must make a fire. How can we make a fire?—Ah! I know. Give me the glass from your watch. I will take the glass from my watch. I will put the two glasses together. I will put water between them.—Now the sun will make a fire for us."

They made a fire and cooked the eggs. Spillet and Neb had not yet come.

The sun went down. They shut the door of the house. They went to sleep.

"Why do not Spillet and Neb come back?" asked Pencroft. "Have they found Harding? Perhaps we should go and look for them."

There was a cry.

"What was that?" cried Herbert. "I heard something!"

The cry was heard again: "Pencroft! Where are you?"

"Here I am!" cried Pencroft. He went out of the door.

It was Spillet and Neb coming back.

"Have you found Harding?" asked Pencroft.

"No," said Spillet.

"Look at our fine house!" said Pencroft.

"Have you any food?" asked Spillet.

"Yes—eggs and shell fish," said Pencroft.

"Where is Top?" asked Herbert.

"He hasn't come," said Pencroft.

They lay down by the fire and went to sleep.

Four

HARDING IS FOUND

It was night, but day was near.

There was a noise at the door.

Pencroft got up. "What was that?" he said. He touched Spillet. He said, "There is someone trying to open the door."

"Someone?" said Spillet, "—yes, but who is it? Are there any people on the island?"

"There is only one person outside the door, and we are three. So we are safe. It is safe to open the door."

Pencroft said, "I will look through a hole in the door." He looked. "There is no one there," he said. "I see no one.—It is a ghost*!"

The sound was heard again. Pencroft opened the door. Top came in.

Top ran to Neb. Neb got up. Top ran to the door.

"He wants to show us where Harding is. He has found Harding and wants to show us where he is."

Top ran. The three men ran after him.

The sky became red. The sun came up.

Top ran to the north. The men followed. They came to a mountain. Top ran into a cave. There was Harding! He was at the foot of the mountain.

Harding's eyes were shut.

"He is dead!" cried Neb.

Pencroft touched Harding's hands and face. "No," he said, "he is not dead."

Herbert brought water and made Harding drink. He opened his eyes. He looked at the three men.

"Where is the balloon?" he said. "Ah! I remember. I fell into the sea. Then I came out of the water—but after that I do not remember." —He put his hands on the grass.

"Grass!" he said. "I do not remember grass where I fell. There was no grass. Is the sea near here?"

"No," said Pencroft, "the sea is not near. It is two miles from here."

"But that cannot be! When I came out of the sea I was almost dead. How did I walk two miles? Did someone carry me?"

"No," said Spillet. "There are no men on the island. No one carried you."

"Then how did I come here?" asked Harding.

Harding got up. They walked to the sea.

"I came out of the water here," he said. "Look! Look!

There were marks of feet.

"Those are not the marks of my feet," said Harding.

"Those are the marks of shoes. I have no shoes. My shoes are in the sea! Whose feet are these? Is there a ghost on the island?"

"Ghosts do not have shoes," said Pencroft.

Five

IS THERE A GHOST?

The sun came up. The men went to the sea and washed their hands and faces. Then they came back to the house.

"What can we have to eat?" said Harding.

"Shell fish, or eggs," answered Pencroft.

"Is that all?" said Harding.

"Yes," said Pencroft, "that is all."

"There are eggs," said Harding. "If there are eggs there are birds. There are birds in the forest. We will have a bird to eat."

"How can we kill a bird? We have no guns," said Spillet. "Perhaps we can throw stones at the birds and kill one."

"Perhaps we can do that," said Harding. "Come, we will try!"

They went out of the house. They went into the forest. It was a big forest. There were many birds, but the men could not kill the birds. They threw stones, but the birds flew away.

"Where is Top?" said Herbert.

Top was not there. They looked. Then they saw Top.

Near Top there was a dead deer.

"Good Top!" said Harding. "See, Top has killed this deer for us. Now we can eat!"

Near Top there was a dead deer

They took the deer to the house. They cooked it. Then they sat down to eat.

"Oh!" said Spillet, "this deer is hard. It is very hard."

"Ah!" cried Pencroft, "I have broken my tooth*. My tooth is broken!"

Pencroft put his hand to his mouth.

"Look," he said, "here is my tooth!"

Harding looked at the tooth. "That is not a tooth," he said. "That is a shot. It is a bullet*. Was this bullet in the deer?"

"Yes," said Pencroft. "The bullet was in the deer."

"The deer was shot. But there is no gun on the island. There are no men on this island!—The deer was shot by a ghost! A man was carried two miles by a ghost! This is an island of ghosts!"

Six

BOWS AND ARROWS

Harding was the leader. He spoke to the others: "We have many things to do. We must wash our clothes. We must make cooking pots. We must get food; but we have no guns. We must shoot birds for food."

"We cannot make guns," said Pencroft.

"No," said Harding; "we cannot make guns, but we can make bows* and arrows*. Pencroft and Her-

[1] A bullet is the shot which comes from a gun.

bert, will you go and make cooking pots? The earth
near the river is good; you can make cooking pots of
it. Neb, will you go and wash the clothes? Spillet and
I will make bows and arrows."

Neb went to wash the clothes. Pencroft and
Herbert went to make cooking pots. Spillet and
Harding made two bows and some arrows.

They took the bows. Harding said, "We will learn
to shoot."

Pencroft was making a very big cooking pot.

"Look at that white tree," said Harding. "We will
shoot at that white tree."

Spillet took the bow. He pulled. He pulled. Then
he let the arrow go. The arrow flew through the air.
It hit the cooking pot in Pencroft's hands.

"Oh!" cried Pencroft, "you have broken my
cooking pot!"

Neb was washing the clothes.

Harding said: "You do not know how to shoot!
I will shoot. See; I hold the bow like this. I hold the
arrow like this. Now!"

He shot the arrow.

"Ah! Ah!" cried Neb. "The arrow hit me!"

"It is not hard to make a bow and arrows," said
Harding, "but it is very hard to shoot with a bow."

Seven

DEATH UNDER WATER

"Let us go and see the island," said Harding. "We think that there are no men on the island, but we do not know this. We have found a bullet in the deer. Who shot the deer? If there is a man on the island, we must know if he is a friend. We must know the island: we may be here for a long time."

They took their bows and arrows and went to see the island. They went to the top of Black Mountain. This is the island. They drew a map and put names on it.

They saw a volcano.[1]

They saw a big lake*. They called it Blue Lake. Harding said, "Perhaps there are fish in the lake. I like fish." They went down the mountain. They came to the lake.

Harding looked at the lake. "Perhaps there are fish in the lake," he said. "We will catch some fish and eat them."

They went down to the lake. Herbert walked in front. He looked into the water to see the fish. Top went with him. Herbert cried out, "Look! A fish! A big fish!"

A very big fish put its head out of the water.

[1] A volcano is a mountain from which fire comes.

A*

Harding shot an arrow at it. The arrow hit the fish. Top jumped into the water. The big fish took Top in its mouth. It went down under the water.

"Oh, my dog," cried Harding, "my dear little dog!"

The water became red.

"The fish has killed Top!" cried Harding.

Then Top was thrown out of the water! He was thrown out like a ball! He fell at Harding's feet.

"I saw a man's arm!" said Neb, "a black arm."

"No man can live under the water," said Spillet.

"It is the ghost!" cried Neb.

After a short time the fish came up. They pulled the fish onto the land. Harding looked at it.

"There!" he said, "that is where my arrow hit it."

"The fish was not killed by your arrow," said Spillet. "Look at this big hole here. That was not made by an arrow. Something has cut the fish."

"Did a man or an animal do that?" asked Harding. "A man could not live under the water. An animal could not throw this dog up onto the land."

"It is a ghost," said Neb. "It is the Ghost of the Island!"

Eight

LAKE HOUSE

"It is a beautiful lake," said Spillet.

"I see where the water comes in," said Harding.

"The water comes into the lake here. But where does the water go out? I do not know where the water goes out. Let us find the place where the water goes out. There was a big rock at the other end of the lake."

They went along the side of the lake. They came to the other end of the lake. There was a big rock at the end of the lake. They saw some trees in front of the rock. Harding went to the trees. Harding went in among the trees.

"The river cannot go out through that rock," said Spillet.

Harding called them. "I have found it!" he said. He threw a bit of wood into the river. The bit of wood went down under the rock.

"Come here," he said. "Come behind these trees. There is a big hole in the rock."

Behind the trees they saw a big hole in the rock. They went through the hole. They were in a big cave. They saw steps. The steps went up. They came to another cave. There were holes in the side of the cave. The holes were like windows. The sunlight came through the holes.

"See," said Harding, "this is our new house. We will bring our things here—our cooking pots, and bows and arrows. We will make tables and beds and all that we need."

"How can we make those things?" said Spillet. "We have only our hands. We cannot cut wood with our hands."

"Bow! Wow!"

Top threw himself against the wall of the cave. *"Bow! Wow!"*

"What is it, Top?" said Harding.

"I think," said Neb, "that I saw the wall of the cave move!"

Harding looked at the rock. He hit it. "That rock cannot move," he said.

Nine

A BOX FROM THE SEA

Harding said, "We must make tables and beds and other things for our new house. We have no tools*. Thousands of years ago men made tools; they made tools out of stone. We must make tools out of stone."

Pencroft sat under a tree. He hit one stone against another stone; he tried to make tools. He could not make tools. He hit his hand with the stone. "Oh! Oh!" he cried, "I have hit my hand. I cannot do this. I will go to the sea and put my hand in the water."

Pencroft went to the sea. He saw a big box near the sea. He said, "Where did that box come from? Did it come from the sea?" He opened the box. It was full of tools and guns and all the things which they needed.

He called Harding and Spillet.

"The box has been brought by the sea. It has come

from some ship. Now we can make things for the new house."

They carried the box away.

Pencroft looked at the place where the box was. He said, "That box was not brought by the sea. It did not come out of the sea. There is no water in it, and it is too heavy. Where did that box come from? Who brought it? How did it come?"

Ten

THE PIRATE SHIP

The new house was ready. There were two rooms. One was a bedroom; the other was a sitting-room. There were tables and beds and all the things needed. There were pictures on the walls.

Harding said, "Now we will make a ship. We will make a ship to take us back to our home."

They began to make a ship.

They had worked all day. They were sitting in the house.

"Top always sits in the same place," said Spillet. "He sits and looks at the wall. Why does he do that?"

"That is the part of the wall which moved," said Neb. "Top thinks that there is someone there."

"The rock cannot move," said Harding.

They heard a noise. It was the sound of a gun. They ran to the window. They looked out. There was a ship near the island.

"It is a pirate ship"

"What is that ship?" said Harding. "Is it an English ship? Can we go back to England on that ship?"

"No," said Pencroft, "it is not an English ship. It has a black flag; it is a pirate[1] ship. I knew a pirate; he was Bob Harvey. He was a very bad man. I will go to the ship. I will find out what ship it is."

Night came and Pencroft went out of the cave. He went down to the sea and took off his clothes. He went into the sea. He came to the ship, and went up onto it. He saw some men. There were thirty men. One man was speaking; it was Bob Harvey.

Bob Harvey said, "This is a beautiful island. We will stay here. We will keep our things here. We will build houses here."

"Perhaps there are men on the island," said one of the pirates.

"I shall kill them. When day comes we will go to the land and see if there are any men. If there are any men or women or children, we will kill them."

A man saw Pencroft. Pencroft jumped over the side of the ship. He jumped into the sea. The man shot at him, but he did not hit him. Pencroft came to the land. He told the other men what he had heard.

[1] Pirates are bad men who live in a ship and fight against other ships and take their money.

Eleven

THE FIGHT

"We must make ready our guns," said Harding.
"There are rocks which go out into the sea. We will go
to the end of those rocks. We will shoot at the boats
as they come."

They went to sleep. When day came, they took
their guns, and went to the end of the rocks. A boat
came down from the ship. It came down onto the
water. Ten men got into the boat. The boat came
near the rocks. They heard the pirates talking: "We
will kill all the people," said one pirate.

"Now!" said Harding. They shot at the men in
the boat. Three men were killed. The boat turned
round and went back to the ship.

"Quick!" cried Harding. "They will shoot at
these rocks. Run back to the forest."

They ran. The ship began to shoot at the rocks
with its big guns.

They came to the forest. The men in the ship saw
them. They began to shoot at the forest.

"We must go to the house," said Harding.

They reached the cave. They looked out of the
window of the cave. Four boats were near the ship;
they were ready to go to the land. Men were getting
into the boats.

Then there was a great explosion

Then there was a great explosion.[1] The whole ship was thrown up out of the sea. It came down in two pieces. The boats and men went down under the water. All the pirates were dead!

Harding, Spillet and Pencroft went down to the sea. The broken ship lay on a rock not far from the land. They waited till the sea went out. Then they walked out to the ship.

"We will take things from this ship to make our ship," said Harding. "There are many useful things in this ship.

"What hit the ship?" asked Harding. "Why did it go up in the air like that? Perhaps the gun-powder in the ship caught fire and exploded. Was that it?"

Pencroft was looking at a small black thing which he held in his hand.

"What is that thing?" asked Harding.

"This thing tells me what hit the ship," said Pencroft.

"What is it?" asked Harding.

"It is part of a torpedo."[2] said Pencroft. "A torpedo hit the pirate ship."

"Where did the torpedo come from?" asked Spillet. "There was no other ship! Did the ghost send the torpedo?"

---

[1] Gun-powder *explodes*. When gun-powder explodes there is an *explosion*. (Gun-powder is the powder which is put in guns.)

[2] A torpedo is a thing sent under the water by a *war-ship*. The torpedo is full of explosives. When the torpedo hits the ship, it explodes and makes a big hole in the ship.

Twelve

KING OF THE ISLAND

It was winter. The men were working at their ship. They were working very hard. Pencroft was giving all the orders; Pencroft was a seaman.

Herbert looked up. He said, "The sky is very dark. There will be rain."

"No," said Pencroft, "there will not be rain. The sky is dark because of the volcano."

"Where is Top?" asked Herbert. "I have not seen Top all day. I will go and look for Top."

Herbert soon came back.

"Come quickly," he cried. "Come and see; a door has opened in the wall of our cave."

They ran to the cave. They saw a door open in the side. It was open at the place at which Top had looked. Top was not there.

They heard Top. He had gone through the door.

Harding went through the door. There was a piece of paper on the wall. He read the paper.

My friends,
   I am very ill. I am going to die. Please come to me.

NOMAN

"Ah!" cried Spillet, "Noman. That was the great pirate. He was never caught."

In the lake there was a submarine

They went down through a hole in the rock. They went far. They came to a great cave. In the cave there was a big lake.

As they stood there the cave became full of light. There were lights in the cave!

In the lake there was a submarine. They went into the submarine. There was a room in the submarine. There was a bed in the room. On the bed there was a very old man. They went to the bed. The old man spoke:

"I am Noman," he said. "You have heard about me. I was a pirate. I had a submarine. I went out as a pirate in my submarine. When I was old I sent away all my men. I came to this island and I lived here alone. I was king of this island; I was the only person on it. I saw you come. I helped you. I put Harding in the cave away from the sea. I killed the deer to give you food. I have a dress in which I can go under water: I saved your dog and killed the fish. I put the box of tools and guns there for you. I sent the torpedo against Bob Harvey's ship. I stood near the door in your cave and heard all that you said.—Ah, there is your dog. He knew me."

"Thank you, thank you!" said the four men. "Now tell us, what can we do for you?"

"You can do nothing!" said Noman. "I shall die to-night. Before I die I will give you this big box of gold and jewels. I do not want them. When I am dead open the water-door of my ship. The water will come into the submarine and it will go down.

[1] A *submarine* is a ship which goes under the water.

That will be the end of me. Go now. Come to-night.
I shall be dead."

They went away. Harding put his hand into the
water; then he put his hand to his mouth.

"This is not a lake," he said; "this water comes
from the sea; it is part of the sea. But it is hot: it is
hot sea-water. Why is it hot?"

He put his hand on the rock.

"This rock is very hot," he said. "The volcano is
near this place. On the other side of this rock there is
the volcano. If this rock breaks and the sea-water goes
into the volcano, there will be an explosion!"

That night they went back to the submarine.
Noman was dead. They opened the water-door; the
submarine went down under the water.

Thirteen

WE SHALL ALL BE BURNT ALIVE!

The ship was ready. It was in the water. They
put food and water in it for the journey.

"We will start as soon as it is day," said Harding.
"To-night we shall sleep in our cave for the last time."

They went to bed. They were soon asleep. Hours
passed. The sky was red; fire was coming out of the
volcano. The earth moved. Pieces of rock fell from
the walls of the cave. A piece of rock hit Spillet.
He woke up, and looked round him. The cave was full
of red light. He looked out of the window, and saw

the fire coming from the volcano. He called Harding.
"Come quickly."

"Is it time to go into the ship?" said Harding.
"No," said Spillet. "No.—But look at the volcano."

A big piece of the side of the volcano fell down.
A river of fire came out. The river of fire moved over
the island. It came to the forest. The forest began
to burn. The river of fire moved on over the forest.

"When that river of fire comes to the lake, the
lake will boil," said Harding. "Then this cave will
not be safe. We must go to the top of the mountain.
That will be a safe place."

They went to the top of the mountain. They took
the box of gold and jewels with them. They looked
down. The island was burning: they saw fire every-
where.

"We are in great danger," said Harding, "We
are in very great danger. When we went to see Noman
I noticed that the sea came into that cave, and the
sea-water was hot. The rock was hot. Noman's cave
is very near the volcano. If the wall of rock breaks,
the sea will go into the volcano. Then there will be
a great explosion. The whole island will explode.
Everything will be broken into thousands of pieces.
We shall be burnt, boiled alive, broken to pieces."

"When will that happen?" said Spillet.
"We have one hour to live!" answered Harding.
"Oh, my ship, my beautiful ship," said Pencroft.
"It will be burnt."

"We shall not need a ship," said Harding. "Look round. All the island, its trees, its flowers, everything is burning. After one hour we shall be burning also. Not one living thing will remain!"

They stood, waiting for death. All round them was the noise of fire. The earth moved. The volcano was red. The forests burned.

Herbert was praying.

"Pray for me," said Pencroft.

The river of fire moved on.

Then there was an explosion. The mountains were broken to bits. Big pieces of the island fell into the sea. Nothing was left—only the top of the mountain; and on that mountain-top, now a little island in the sea, there were four men, lying on the ground, and a boy praying in a clear voice.

The boy fell as if dead.

Nothing was heard. There was darkness.

Fourteen

SAVED

The sun came up.

The sea was now quiet. Little waves touched the side of the rock. The four men and the boy lay there. The dog was sitting on Noman's box.

Pencroft opened his eyes. He looked at the sea. He said, "The sea would have been good for our ship."

Harding sat up. "There is no ship," he said, "and there will be no journey."

"No," said Pencroft, "no ship. I worked so hard making that ship. It was a beautiful ship; and now it is burnt."

"We shall stay here till we are dead," said Harding. "We have no food, no water. No ships come here. We shall die here, on this rock."

Pencroft laughed. His laugh woke up Spillet and Neb.

"Why are you laughing?" said Harding, "there is nothing to laugh at."

"Look!" said Pencroft, pointing to the box. "There are jewels, there is gold! We are rich. We can buy the best food and drink in the world. But we shall die because we have not even a bit of bread or a drop of water!"

The sun went higher in the sky. It was very hot. It became hotter and hotter.

"Water! Water!" cried Herbert.

He began to talk about his mother—his home, his friends at school. He did not know what he was saying. Then he fell on his face. Pencroft tried to keep the sun off him. Soon Spillet fell down as if he was dead.

Only Pencroft and Harding remained.

"Which of us will fall first?" said Harding. "Which of us is stronger?"

As Harding spoke the sky seemed to become black. He fell.

Only Pencroft remained.

He took off his coat. "If a ship comes," he said, "we shall need a flag. I will use this coat as a flag."

Top was asleep; or was he dead?
Pencroft opened the box of jewels. He looked at the gold and jewels.

"There is enough money," he said, "for all the rest of our lives. But there is no more life for us. This is the end."

He looked up. He thought that he saw a ship. He thought that he saw Bob Harvey; and Bob Harvey held out a glass of water to him. He put out his hand to take the water—and it was gone! Then he thought that he saw Noman in his submarine. Was it a submarine?

Pencroft looked up again.—He saw a ship. It was an English ship! He held up the coat as a flag. He tried to call out, "Help! Help! Save us!" but his mouth was like dust. He could not make a sound.

Had the men in the ship seen him? The ship sailed on. He cried out. He held up the flag. At last the ship stopped.

A boat came down the side of the ship onto the water.

That is the end of the story. Harding, Pencroft, Herbert, Spillet and Neb went home to England. They were all rich.

Poor Top! Top died on the rock.

He held up the flag

QUESTIONS

1.
1. What is a balloon?
2. How many men were there in the balloon?
3. Was the balloon going up, or down?
4. What did they throw out?

1. What time was it?
2. How many hours passed?
3. What did they cut off?
4. Where did it (3) fall?

1. Who jumped out into the sea?
2. What jumped out after him?
3. How many men jumped down onto the ground?
4. Where did the balloon go?

1. What work did Gideon Spillet do?
2. What was Pencroft?
3. Who was Herbert?
4. Who was Harding's servant?
5. What was the name of the dog?

2.
1. Were the men on a big island?
2. For what was Neb looking?
3. Where did Neb go?

1. Where did Spillet go?
2. Where did Pencroft and Herbert walk?
3. What did they want to find?
4. What did Pencroft find?
5. What must they make at the north end?

1. What did they (Pencroft and Herbert) find in the forest?
2. What cannot they do?
3. What carried the branches?

3.
1. What has Herbert got for dinner?
2. In what will they cook the eggs?
3. What did Pencroft put together?
4. Had Spillet and Neb come?

1. Had Spillet and Neb found Harding?
2. Had Top come?
3. Where did they sleep?

4.
1. What was someone trying to do?
2. Where did Pencroft look?
3. Who came in?

1. What does Top want to show?
2. Where did Top run?
3. Where was Harding?

1. What did Herbert bring?
2. Was there grass where Harding fell?
3. How far away is the sea?
4. Are there any men on the island?

1. What marks were there?
2. Had Harding shoes?
3. Were the marks marks of shoes?

5.
1. What are there in the forest?
2. Have the men guns?
3. How will they kill the birds?

1. What was near Top?
2. What did Pencroft break?

1. (a) Was it a tooth?
   (b) What was it?
2. By what was the deer killed?

6.
1. What must they wash?
2. What must they make?
3. With what will they shoot?
4. Who will wash the clothes?

1. What was Pencroft making?
2. At what will they shoot?
3. What did Spillet's arrow hit?
4. What did Harding's arrow hit?

7.
1. They went to the top of—what?
2. What comes out of a volcano?
3. What name did they give to the lake?

1. What will they catch?
2. What put its head up?
3. What did the fish take?
4. What did the water do?

1. What was thrown out of the water?
2. What did Neb see?
3. What killed the fish?

8.
1. What does not Spillet know?
2. What was there at the end of the lake?
3. Where did the bit of wood go?

1. What did they see behind the trees?
2. What were they in?
3. Where did the steps go?
4. What will they make?

1. Where did Top throw himself?
2. What did Neb see?

9.
1. Of what did men make tools?
2. What did Pencroft hit with a stone?

1. What did Pencroft see near the sea?
2. What was in the box?
3. Had the box come out of the sea?

10.
1. How many rooms were there?
2. What will they make now?

1. At what does Top look?
2. What does Top think?
3. What was the noise?

1. What flag has the ship?
2. What ship is it?
3. To what did Pencroft go?
4. How many men were in the ship?
5. Who was speaking?

1. What will the pirates do to the men on the island?
2. Where did Pencroft jump?
3. What are pirates?

11.
1. Where will they go?
2. What did one pirate say?
3. How many men were killed?

1. Where did they run?
2. Where must they go?
3. How many boats were near the ship?

1. What is an explosion?
2. How many pirates were dead?
3. Where did the ship lie?

1. What had Pencroft in his hand?
2. What hit the ship?

12.
1. What part of the year was it?
2. Why is the sky dark?
3. What has happened to the wall of the cave?

1. Where had Top gone?
2. Who was Noman?
3. What was in the great cave?
4. What was in the lake?
5. Who was in the boat?

1. What did Noman do when he was old?
2. What will Noman give to the men?
3. What must they open when Noman is dead?

1. Where does the water come from?
2. What did Harding say about the rock?
3. What will happen if the rock breaks?

13.
1. When will they go to the ship?
2. What hit Spillet?
3. Whom did Spillet call?

1. What fell?
2. What came out?
3. Where must they go?

1. What is near the volcano?
2. What will go into the volcano?
3. What will happen to the men?

1. How long will they live?
2. About what is Pencroft sad?

1. What was Herbert doing?
2. What fell into the sea?
3. What was left?

14.
1. Where was the dog sitting?
2. At what did Pencroft look?
3. What did Harding say?

1. Where will they die?
2. Who laughed?
3. What can they buy?

1. What did Herbert cry?
2. What did Pencroft try to do?
3. What will Pencroft use as a flag?

1. At what did Pencroft look?
2. What person did Pencroft think he saw?
3. What did the person (2) hold out?
4. What other person did Pencroft think he saw?

1. What did Pencroft see?
2. What did he hold up?
3. Who died on the rock?

PRONUNCIATION OF THE NAMES IN THE STORY

*The symbols shown are those of the International
Phonetic Alphabet*

BOB	bɔb
GIDEON	gidiən
HARDING	hɑːdiŋ
HARVEY	hɑːvi
HERBERT	həːbət
NEB	neb
NOMAN	noumɑn
PENCROFT	penkrɔft
SPILLET	spilit
TOP	tɒp

LIST OF EXTRA WORDS

arrow	6	lake	7
balloon	1	river	2
bows	6	seaman	1
branches	2	shell fish	2
coconut	3	tools	9
ghost	4	writer	1